Publisher: DAVE ELLIOTT
Design: MARK COX
Production: GARRY LEACH, RICHARD BARKER
Editorial Assistant: FRANK WYNNE
With thanks to: STEVE MacMANUS, MATT BROOKER

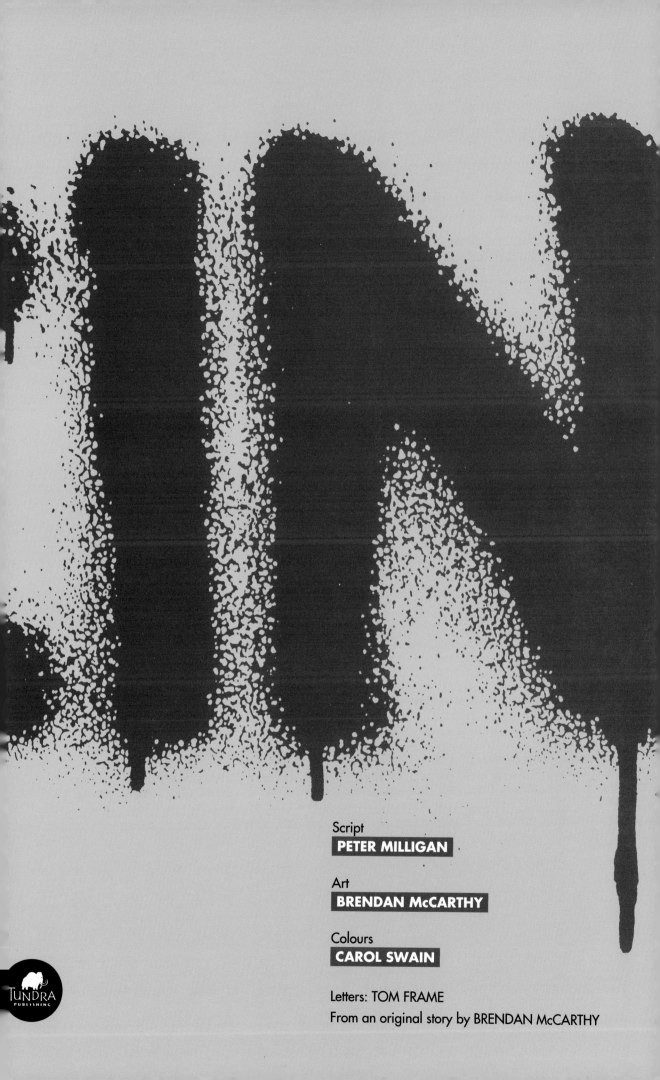

Script
PETER MILLIGAN

Art
BRENDAN McCARTHY

Colours
CAROL SWAIN

Letters: TOM FRAME

From an original story by BRENDAN McCARTHY

TUNDRA
PUBLISHING

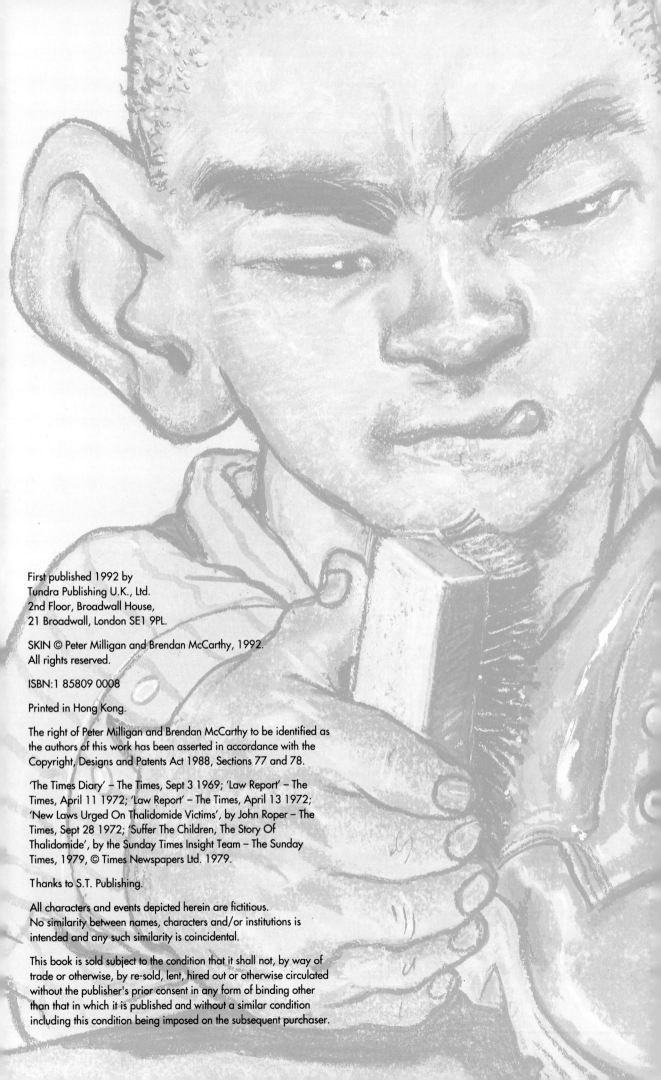

First published 1992 by
Tundra Publishing U.K., Ltd.
2nd Floor, Broadwall House,
21 Broadwall, London SE1 9PL.

ISBN:1 85809 0008

Printed in Hong Kong.

'The Times Diary' – The Times, Sept 3 1969; 'Law Report' – The
Times, April 11 1972; 'Law Report' – The Times, April 13 1972;
'New Laws Urged On Thalidomide Victims', by John Roper – The
Times, Sept 28 1972; 'Suffer The Children, The Story Of
Thalidomide', by the Sunday Times Insight Team – The Sunday
Times, 1979, © Times Newspapers Ltd. 1979.

Thanks to S.T. Publishing.

We've been told that SKIN is tasteless. It certainly has all the usual ingredients: sex, drugs, violence, bad language, deformity, mutilation. But does that make it tasteless? Maybe the very mention of the word THALIDOMIDE is enough to do that.

The idea for a story about Thalidomide began with Brendan McCarthy. In his youth, Brendan was involved in the skinhead culture. One of the skinheads growing up in his part of London had been deformed by the terrible drug, and Brendan began to ask himself what it must be like to be trapped in a body like this. The story grew...

Years later, Brendan collaborated with Peter Milligan, who came from a similar background. Brendan's idea struck a chord with Peter, who also remembered seeing a skinhead with the characteristic foreshortened arms of a "Thalidomide". (It's interesting that the word 'Thalidomide' became a noun — "He is a Thalidomide", "She is a Thalidomide". These mutilated children were the drug; they were the flesh-and-bone equivalent of the chemical equation that created the drug that shaped them.)

That we both saw "Thalidomide Skinheads" in our youth is not wholly surprising. In the early seventies, skinheads were the predominant Urban Youth Culture, it was also the time when the children who had been deformed by Thalidomide – those who survived – were reaching puberty.

SKIN was first commissioned some years ago by Fleetway Publications and was scheduled to appear in its "Adult Comic" CRISIS. When their reproduction company refused to handle SKIN, Fleetway showed the story to their lawyers, who advised them not to publish. Most publishers would have taken such advice. Fleetway was no exception.

Why was SKIN banned? Why have so many subsequent publishers shown great interest in the story only to shy away from it? It's almost as though SKIN itself became a little monster: a deformed creature that people turned their faces from.

Perhaps one of the problems is class, and the way in which this influences how such stories are told. SKIN is about skinheads and is told from the point of view of a fifteen-year-old skinhead, a narrator who doesn't give a toss about leitmotifs and dénouements. He'd probably head-butt you for calling him a narrator. Now, if we had called the story, say, ETON CROP and it had been about a nice, sensitive young Thalidomide from Hampstead who is bullied at school, who writes beautiful poems about his plight and eventually rises above his condition, thereby renewing our faith in the indomitable nature of the human spirit, maybe we wouldn't have had so many problems. But our little skinhead doesn't want to be nice. He just wants the right to be a yob and get his hands inside girls' knickers. His skinhead world is violent. But its violence pales beside the corporate violence of Thalidomide.

So, what about the accusation? Is SKIN tasteless? We hope it is. A story that deals with a young person whose body, whose life is deformed by powerful Multi-National Corporations, who is abandoned by Government and ridiculed as a monster by his peers has an obligation to be tasteless. These things happened to real people in this country.
How tasteful can you get?

PETER MILLIGAN & **BRENDAN McCARTHY.**

"...Faced with the sight of the disintegrated child, passers-by and professionals alike seemed to feel their own mental and physical wholeness at risk. I remember seeing a family with a thalidomide child on the beach. There was always an empty space around them."

– DR NEWMAN.

HALIDOMIDE is the name given to a 'Wonder Drug' invented in Germany in the 1950s by Chemie Grünenthal and marketed as a sedative pill. Chemie Grünenthal claimed that the drug was completely safe for pregnant women. But no adequate tests, which were available at the time, were carried out to discover whether the drug would pass the placenta and therefore affect the unborn child. The result was a wave of horrific birth defects in children who became known as 'Thalidomide Babies'. The effects of Thalidomide are usually associated with grossly foreshortened arms and legs (phocomelia), but the range of deformity was wide, depending on the phase of pregnancy during which the drug was taken. It is a horrific and chastening thought that, generally, the 'Thalidomide Babies' who survived and grew were those with less extreme malformations. Babies were born without eyes and ears, sometimes without a brain, with limbless trunks, cleft faces, closure of the anus and with catastrophic internal deformities.

The plight of the 'Thalidomide Children' and their families was compounded by the drug companies involved, by governments and, particularly in Britain, by the creaking machinations of the legal system.

In Britain in the Sixties, the Profumo Affair was thought of as the scandal of the decade. It wasn't. The real scandal began in Germany with a chemical equation. The real scandal was Thalidomide.

Kunz first produc... ...xic sub
...uman distress it would cau
complex structure. But it con...

for thalidomide children

country to · fact getting an interest in the · from being a next fr
he parents. · charitable trust. The defendant · must be satisfied ·
under the · company was not entitled to treat · was acting in
the chil- · 374 individual claims as one global · to a r
n if they · claim.
1963 Act, · If the court held ..
dvised to · of a nex

alidomide chi

cy—and she did not know until · h
that doctor had died and she · w
to another doctor in 1968 · h
baby was a thalidomide · f
So she was thought to have · t
good case under the 1963 Act
...se she did not know the facts
Her boy had quite
...sonable prospect of a fairly
...mal life in the future
...ere just two out of 260
to ...ced was

aws urged o

compensation if it
they had been
drug...

This story takes place in the early Seventies, during what might be called the 'Golden Age' of skinheads. Without wanting to go into any deep cultural analysis, a few words about these skinheads might be useful. The skins of this period had yet to become politicised and used as storm troopers of the Right-Wing: they were, simply, a peculiarly British, mainly urban, youth culture. Their roots come from the British 'Mods' and the West-Indian 'Rude Boys'. It is ironic that a movement which has become a byword for White Racist Nationalism had its roots in Black Caribbean culture.

Like most British working-class youth cultures, skinhead life centred around music, fashion, sex, fighting, football, alcohol and having a laugh – preferably at some other tosser's expense. The music was Reggae, which had developed from the Ska music and the Blue Beat of the Rude Boys – songs like Liquidator and Skinhead Moonstomp. The clothes were Ben Sherman shirts, Levi's, Doc Marten boots, Sta Press trousers, loafers, brogues, white socks and black crombies.

Abuse of all forms was held in very high esteem in skinhead culture. The language was violent and crude and often very funny. For a reader unfamiliar with British slang, some of the language used in the story might be a little mystifying. For instance 'Wanker' is a general term of abuse, but it also refers to the verb to wank, meaning to masturbate. 'Big Bender' means, literally, a large homosexual, but is used as an alternative to wanker, which in turn is sometimes replaced by 'Tosser' – a milder insult.

The meanings of other curious expressions can generally be inferred from their context but, if not, bollocks.

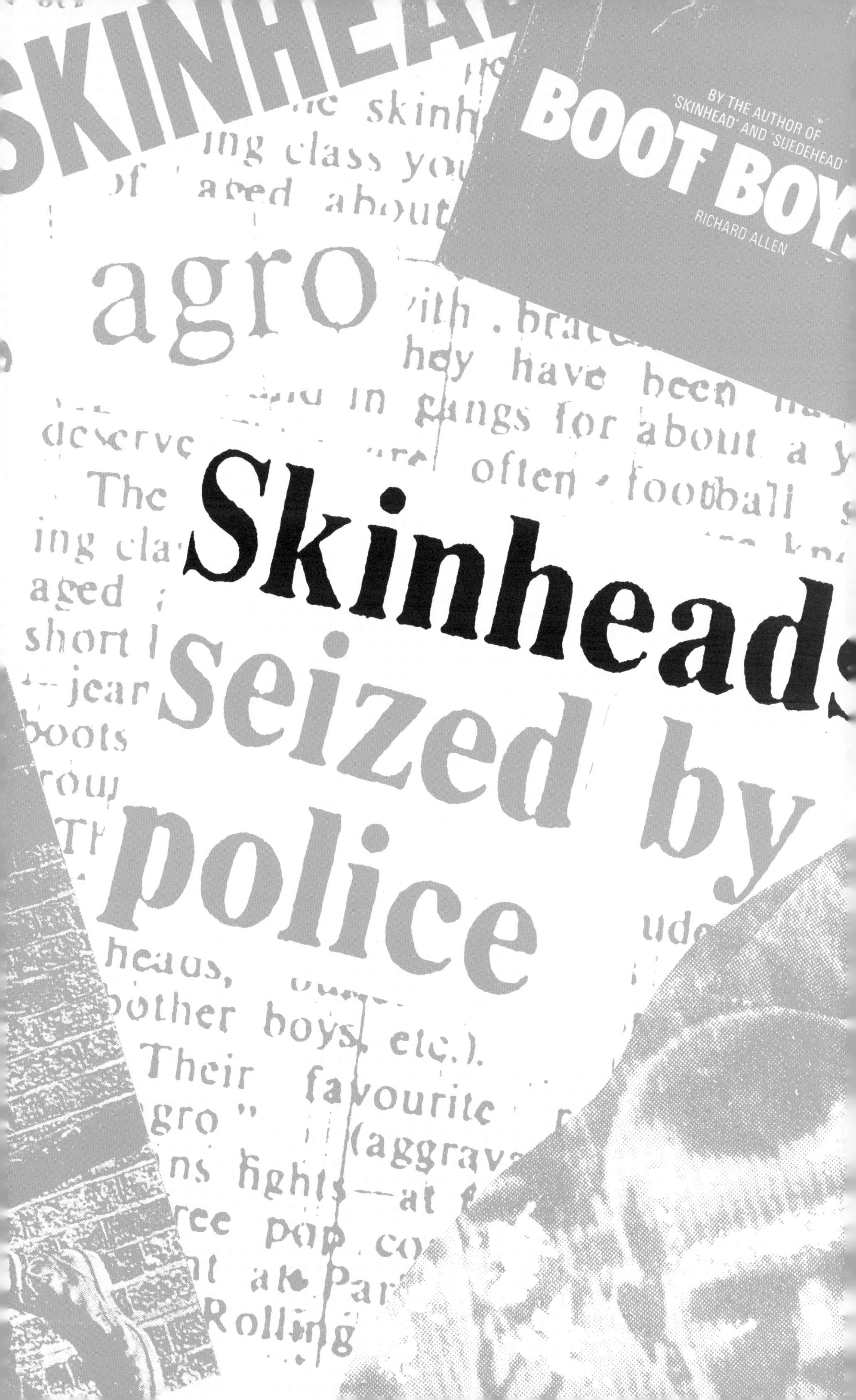

SKINHEAD

BOOT BOYS

BY THE AUTHOR OF
'SKINHEAD' AND 'SUEDEHEAD'

RICHARD ALLEN

agro

Skinheads

seized by

police

ENGLAND

EARLY SEVENTIES

AND ALL THAT

THE WANKERS HAD A WORD FOR IT.

WE SAW IT IN A BOOK **CROSSEYED RUBY** SHOWED US. PHOCOMELIA. RUBY SAID THAT'S GREEK AND MEANS SEAL LIMB. **FUKKIN SEAL LIMB!**

POXY LITTLE FLIPPERS STICKING OUT THE SIDE OF HIS BODY. BUT SEALS CAN **CLAP** THEIR FLIPPERS AND THAT, CAN'T THEY? **MARTIN** COULDN'T.

MARTIN WAS ONE OF THOSE **THALIDOMIDE** BABIES. HIS MUM TOOK A PILL TO STOP HERSELF PUKING WHEN SHE WAS PREGNANT. BET SHE PUKED ENOUGH WHEN SHE SAW MARTIN.

MARTIN LOOKED LIKE A WANKER BUT OF COURSE HE COULDN'T EVEN DO THAT. **WANK,** I MEAN. COULDN'T SHAKE HIS OWN KNOB, WIPE HIS ARSE, COMB HIS HAIR. BUT HE DIDN'T NEED TO COMB HIS HAIR.

MARTIN ACHITSON MIGHT HAVE LOOKED LIKE A WANKER WHO COULDN'T WANK, HE MIGHT HAVE BEEN A SEAL BOY, BUT HE WAS ONE OF **US.** WE CALLED HIM **MARTIN 'ATCHET.**

HE WAS A SKIN.

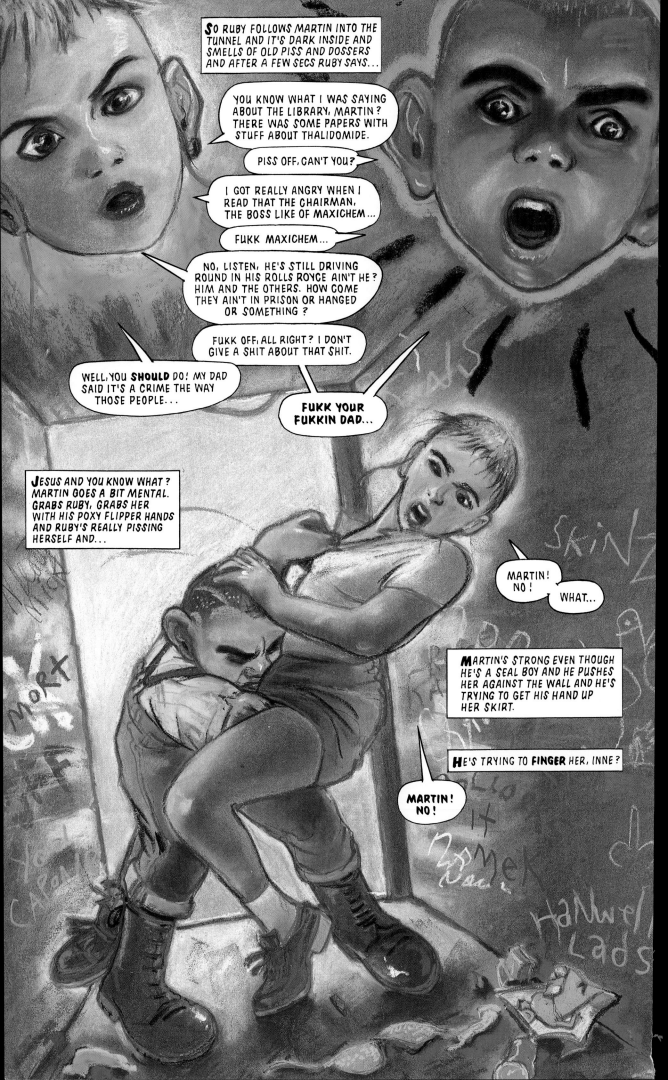

SO OUTSIDE IT'S PISSING DOWN AND MARTIN KICKS OUT AT EVERY FUKKIN THING AND EVERY TOSSER THAT GETS IN HIS WAY.

HE GIGGLES A BIT AS THE RAIN HITS HIS BONCE AND HE DON'T GIVE A **FUKK** NO MORE, NOT A **FUKKIN FUKK**.

OI!

RUBY!

RUBY LIVES HERE BUT HER OLD MAN WOULD KILL HIM IF MARTIN KNOCKED THIS LATE SO HE THROWS THIS BIT OF BRICK UP AT HER WINDOW LIKE.

KRASH!

MARTIN? MARTIN, WHAT YOU DOING, YOU SMASHED THE-

MEET ME OUTSIDE THE LIBRARY IN **FIFTEEN MINUTES.**

I **CAN'T,** MARTIN, YOU'RE **BLEEDING!** WHAT'S **HAPPENED?**

AND THEN THE WHOLE STREET STARTS TO WAKE UP SO MARTIN LEGS IT.

HE DON'T CARE ABOUT **RUNNING** NO MORE. DON'T GIVE A FUKK ABOUT FALLING OVER AND FUKKIN UP HIS FACE OR ANY FUKKIN THING.

MARTIN 'ATCHET'S A FUKKIN **SKIN!**

AND HE HEARS HOW THE BOSSES OF **MAXICHEM**, THE COMPANY IN THIS COUNTRY THAT FLOGGED LITTLE PILLS OF THALIDOMIDE TO WANKERS LIKE MARTIN'S MUM WERE STILL DRIVING IN THEIR **BIG CARS** . . .

DRIVING IN THEIR **BIG CARS** WITH THEIR **BIG ARMS** AND THEIR **BIG LEGS** AND NO ONE GAVE A **FUKK** REALLY.

AND AFTER IT'S ALL DONE THEY DON'T SAY NOTHING FOR A BIT, THEY JUST SIT THERE SORT OF BREATHING.

THEN MARTIN STARTS MAKING THIS FUNNY KINDA **SNIFFLING** NOISE.

LIKE HE WAS AN **ANIMAL** OR SOMETHING.

THE WANKER'S **CRYING**, INNE ?

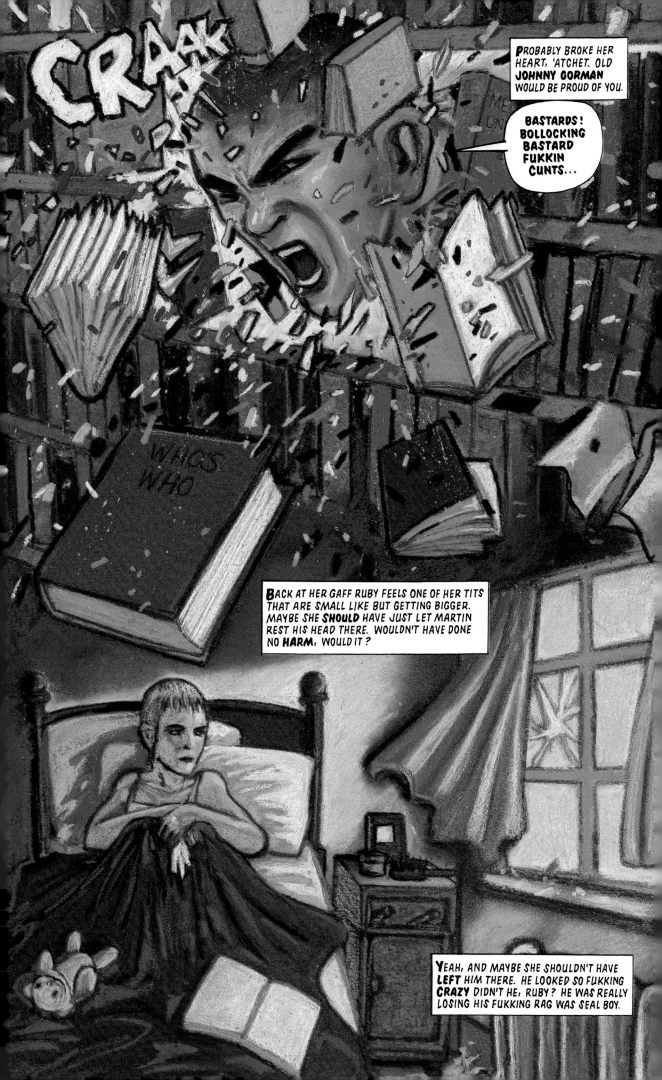

POOR OLD **CROSSEYED RUBY** WENT TO HIS **FUNERAL** AND A FEW WEEKS LATER HAD HER OPERATION AND SHE WASN'T **CROSSEYED** NO MORE.

AND EVEN JOHNNY GORMAN TRIED TO GET OFF WITH HER BUT SHE WOULDN'T LET HIM AND SHE STOPPED BEING A SKINHEAD BIRD AND WENT TO **COLLEGE** INSTEAD.

MARTIN'S MUM DIDN'T GO TO HIS FUNERAL BECAUSE SHE'S A FAT OLD SLAG WHO AIN'T LEFT THE HOUSE SINCE HE WAS BORN.

MARTIN'S **DAD** WENT AND HE CRIED HIS FUKKIN EYES OUT. JOHNNY GORMAN ALWAYS SAID HE WAS A **BUMBOY.**

AND THAT'S THE FUKKIN STORY OF **MARTIN ATCHISON** THEN. HE MIGHT HAVE LOOKED LIKE A WANKER WHO COULDN'T WANK BUT HE WAS ONE OF **US.** WE CALLED HIM **MARTIN 'ATCHET.**

HE WAS A SKIN. ALL RIGHT?

THE END

FINAL WORD

The Thalidomide Children eventually received compensation, though only after a frustrating, decade-long struggle against what often seemed to be an establishment circle of Governments, Legal Institutions and drugs companies.

That Thalidomide, under the trade name Kevadon, was not more widely used in the United States can be attributed largely to the work of Dr. Frances Kelsey, a physician with the Food and Drug Administration. Kelsey was decorated by President Kennedy for her role in stopping the drug being marketed in America.

BRENDAN McCARTHY

ike most people, Brendan McCarthy was born a skinhead. He spent his youth hanging about with other skins and drawing skinhead comics in the back of his maths exercise books.

Twenty years later he returned to the idea of skinheads in comics and invented SKIN.

He explains: "It has taken a lot of effort to get this comic strip out to the public; we've had to get around

STEPHANIE HAUMUELLER

serious amounts of repression and censorship, but it's been worth it. SKIN is a landmark in British comics, one of the best comic strips ever - offhand, I can't think of anything that betters SKIN."

He has produced a small body of influential work over the years - highly intense and individual creations: *Strange Days*, *Paradax*, *Electric Hoax*, etc. "I don't see comics as just graphic art, I come from a painting background. I prefer fine art. What pop music is to classical music, comics are to painting."

Brendan McCarthy has generously donated the artwork for SKIN to the London Tate Gallery as a bequest to the nation.

He continues to design for TV, cinema and Rock videos, his most recent topping the US and UK Hit Parades.

With absolutely no interest in anything other than comics and skinhead memorabilia, McCarthy now lives in a reclusive twilight world where he observes and appreciates the performances of the "International Orchestra" as they rehearse and perfect their greatest work; "The New World Order"

Brendan McCarthy is a DIAMOND GEEZER.

PETER MILLIGAN

eter Milligan was born in Prague in 1883. Some of his early work includes *The Electric Hoax*, *Bad Company*, *Strange Days* and *Sooner or Later*. A string of unsatisfactory love-affairs, his relationship with his father - a self-made man who cared nothing for his son's literary aspirations, his own inflexible intellectual honesty and near-psychopathic sensitivity and the "hunger years" of post 1918 Berlin, finally broke his health.

Nevertheless, he has produced more recent works: *Skreemer*, *Paradax!* and the current cult comic *Shade, The Changing Man*. Later this year will see the publication of a controversial piece called *The Enigma*, and, later, *Rogan Gosh*, the groundbreaking omni-comprehensive post-cubist work of genius created with Brendan McCarthy. An outrageous story entitled *Captain Cracking* will also appear soon, springing fully formed and perfumed from the self-same loins of Milligan and McCarthy.

Milligan is also working on a number of film screenplays, and is known in Hollywood as 'the find of the decade'.

He died in 1924.